JEROME KERN: PIANO SOLOS

WISE PUBLICATIONS
LONDON/NEW YORK/SYDNEY

EXCLUSIVE DISTRIBUTORS:
MUSIC SALES LIMITED
8/9 FRITH STREET,
LONDON W1V 5TZ, ENGLAND.
MUSIC SALES PTY LIMITED
120 ROTHSCHILD AVENUE,
ROSEBERY, NSW 2018,
AUSTRALIA.

THIS BOOK © COPYRIGHT 1990 BY
WISE PUBLICATIONS
ORDER NO.AM81498
ISBN 0.7119.2384.1

COVER AND BOOK DESIGN BY PEARCE MARCHBANK STUDIO
COMPILED BY PETER EVANS
ARRANGED BY FRANK BOOTH
MUSIC PROCESSED BY MUSICPRINT

MUSIC SALES' COMPLETE CATALOGUE LISTS THOUSANDS OF TITLES AND IS
FREE FROM YOUR LOCAL MUSIC SHOP, OR DIRECT FROM MUSIC SALES LIMITED.
PLEASE SEND £1.75 IN STAMPS FOR POSTAGE TO MUSIC SALES LIMITED,
8/9 FRITH STREET, LONDON W1V 5TZ.

PRINTED IN THE UNITED KINGDOM BY
J.B. OFFSET PRINTERS (MARKS TEY) LIMITED, MARKS TEY, ESSEX.

A FINE ROMANCE

MUSIC BY JEROME KERN
WORDS BY DOROTHY FIELDS

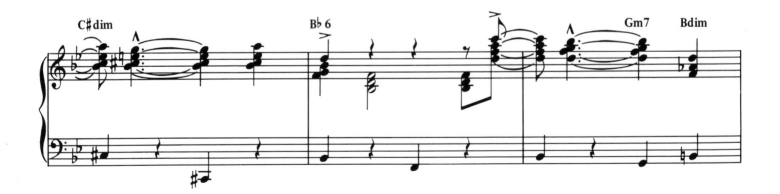

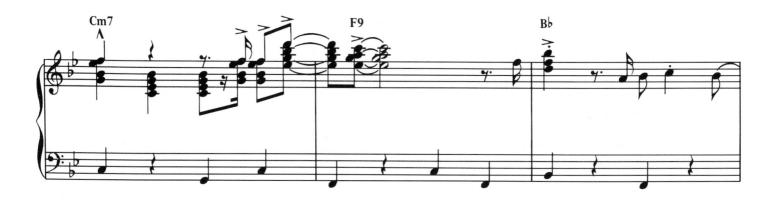

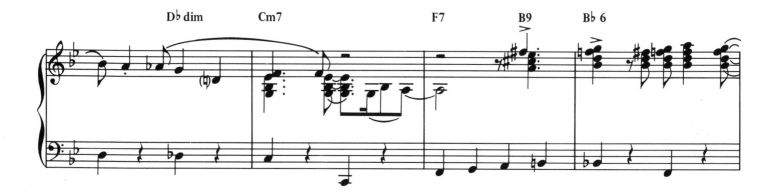

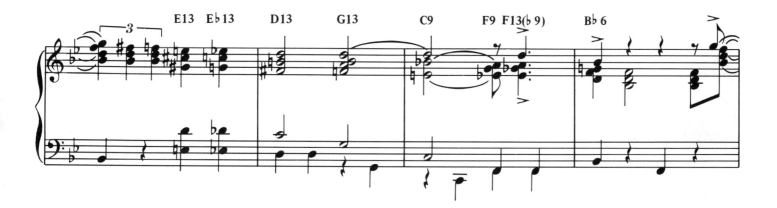

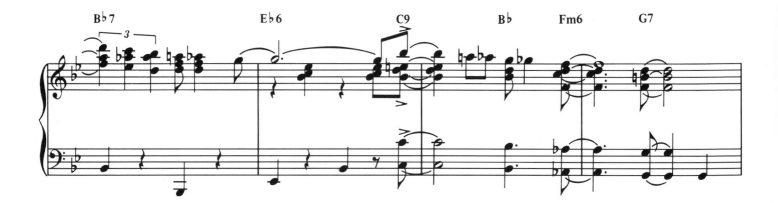

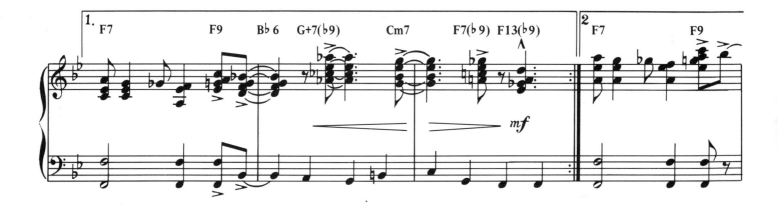

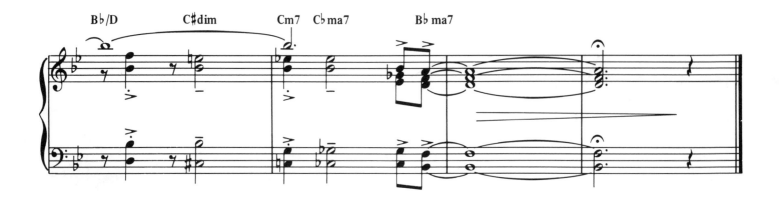

ALL THE THINGS YOU ARE

MUSIC BY JEROME KERN
WORDS BY OSCAR HAMMERSTEIN II

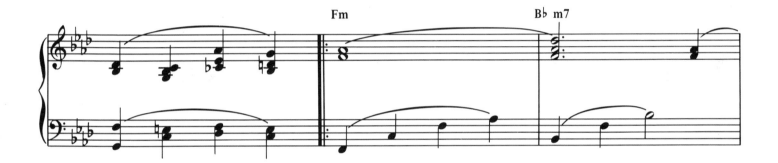

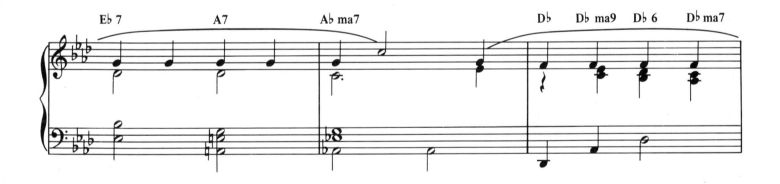

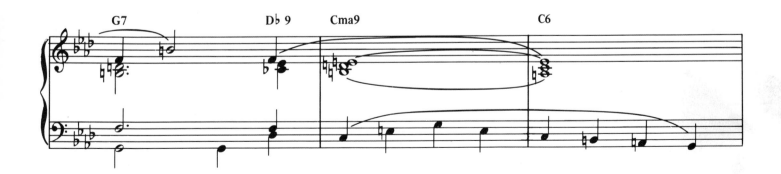

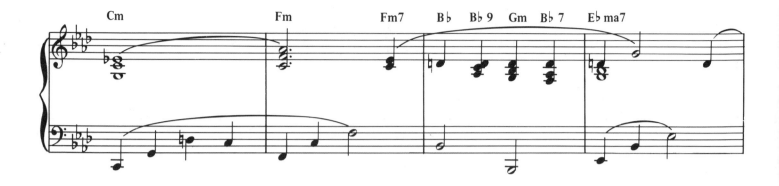

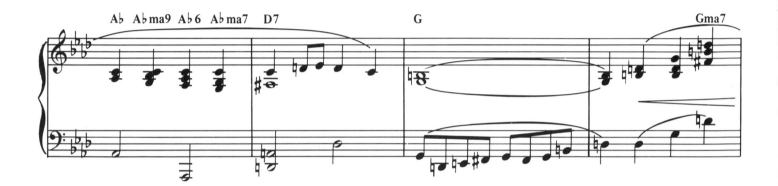

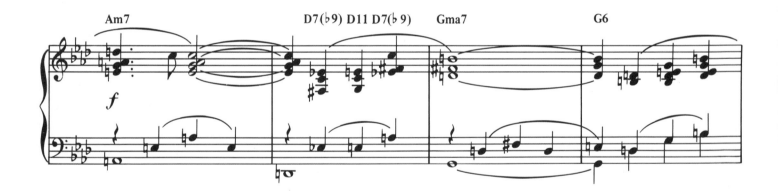

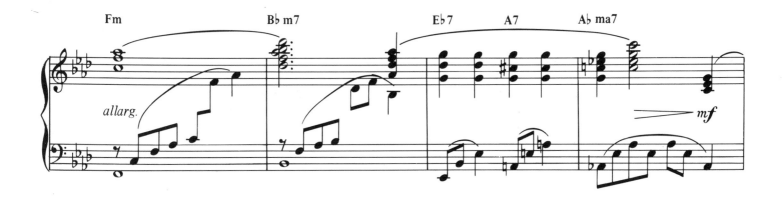

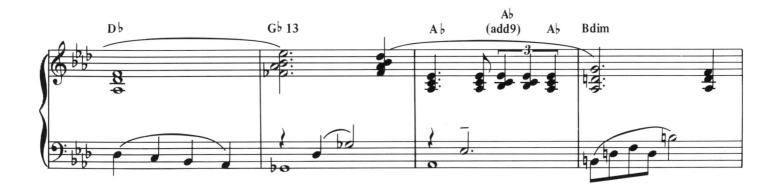

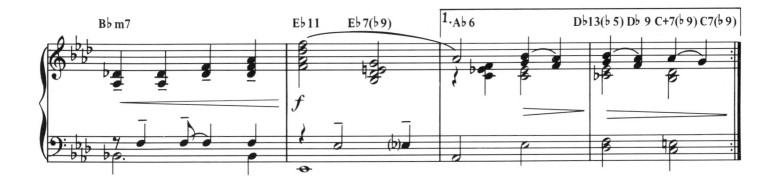

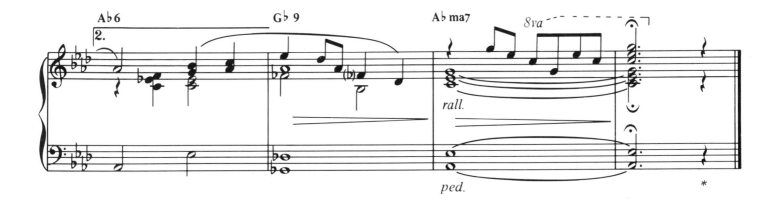

DEARLY BELOVED

MUSIC BY JEROME KERN
WORDS BY JOHNNY MERCER

Fairly fast, with a jazz feel

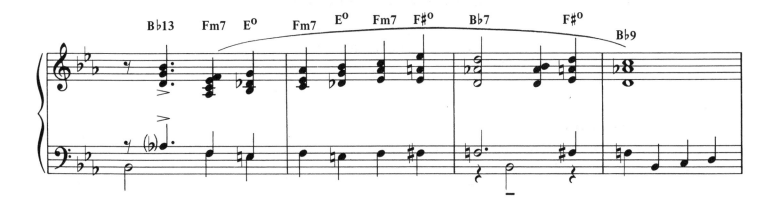

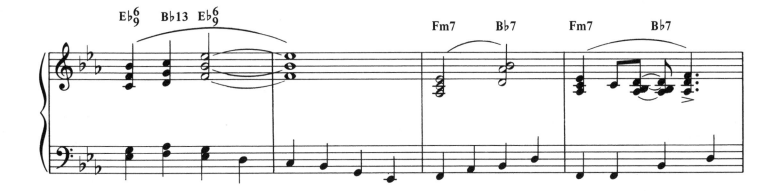

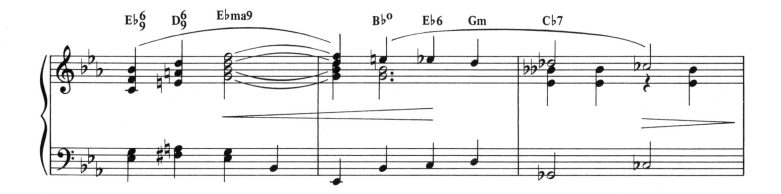

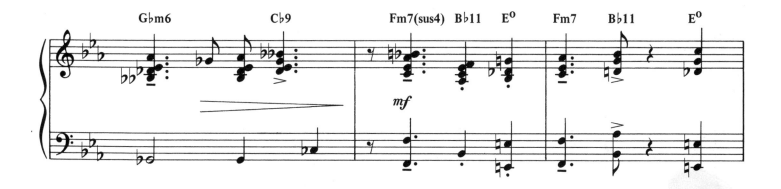

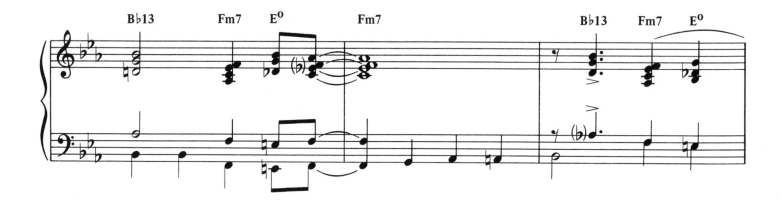

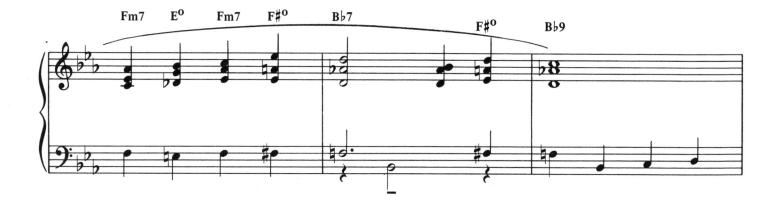

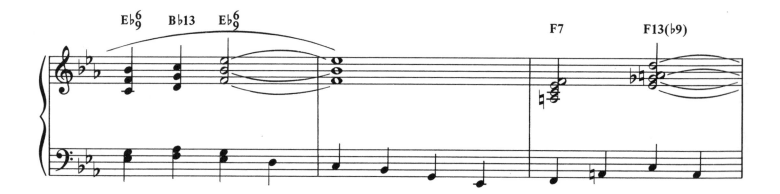

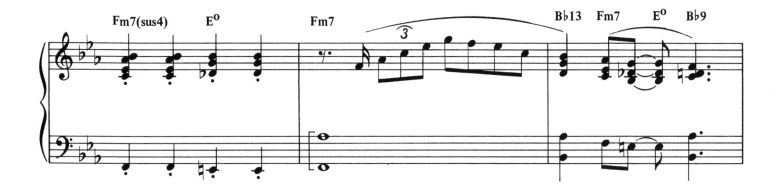

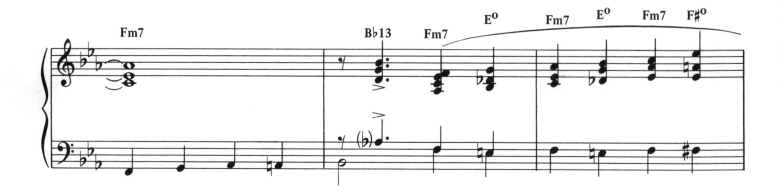

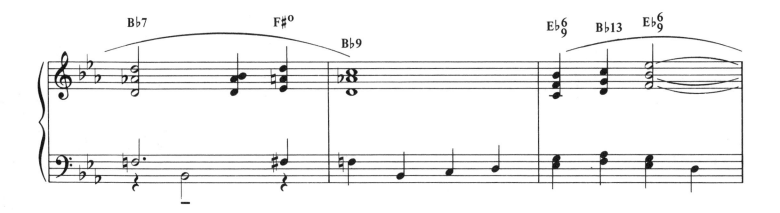

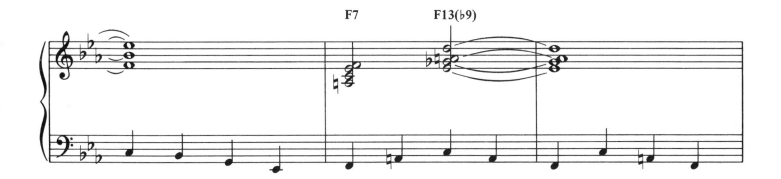

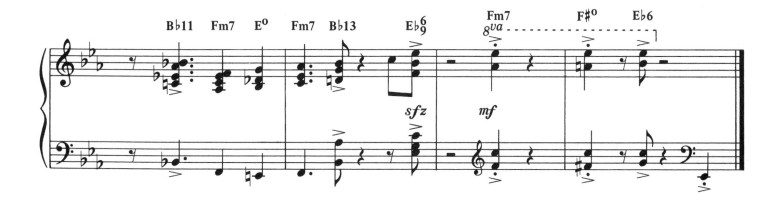

BILL

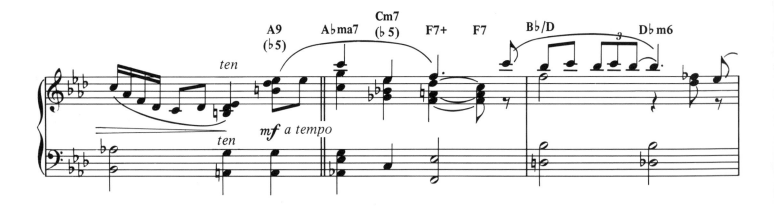

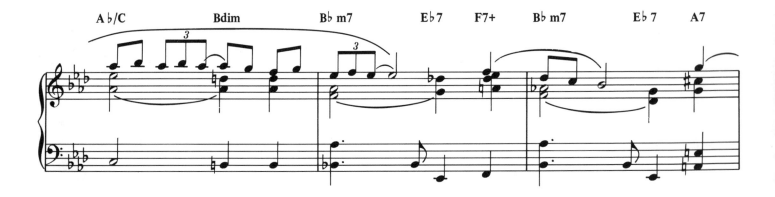

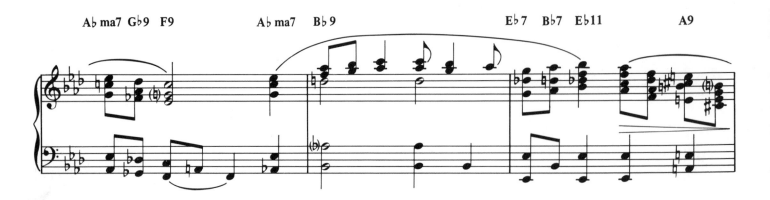

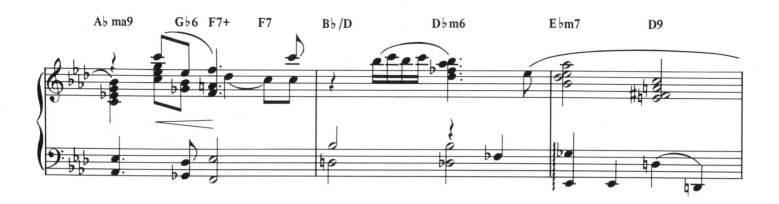

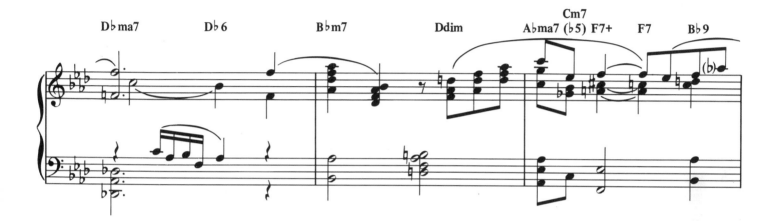

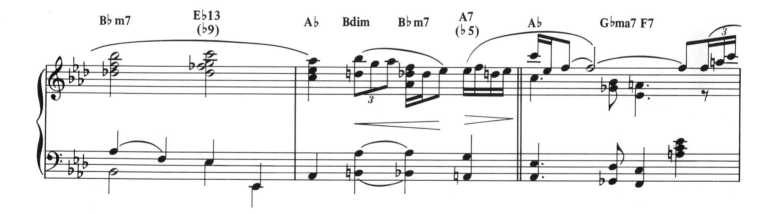

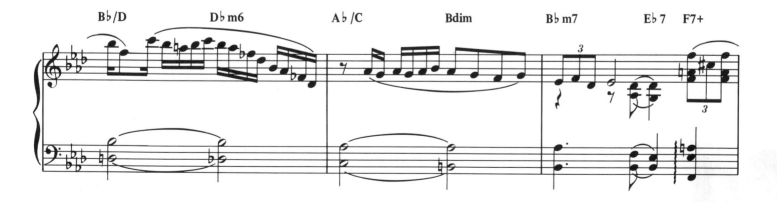

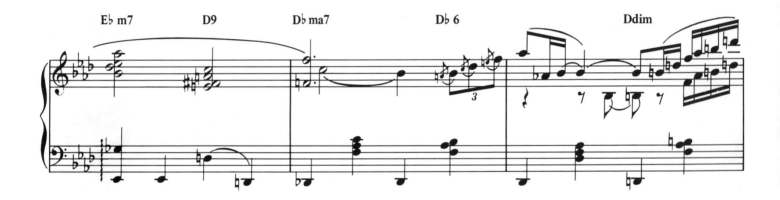

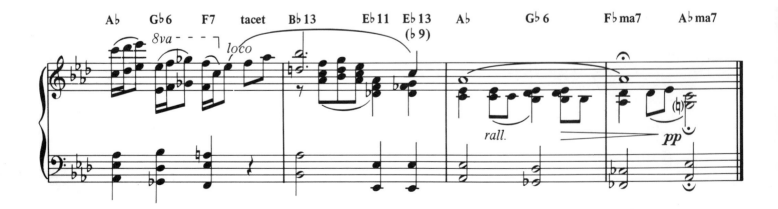

I'M OLD FASHIONED

MUSIC BY JEROME KERN
WORDS BY JOHNNY MERCER

Moderately

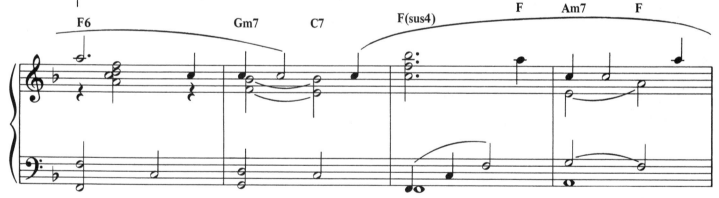

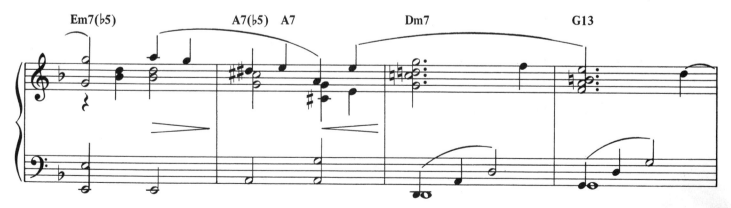

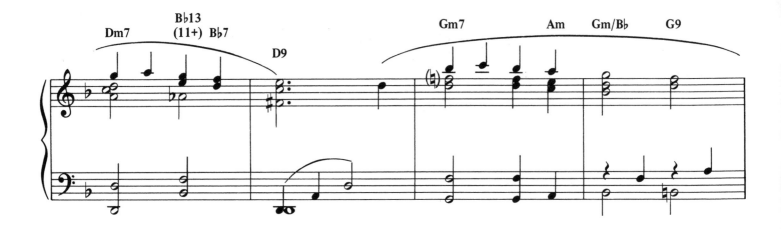

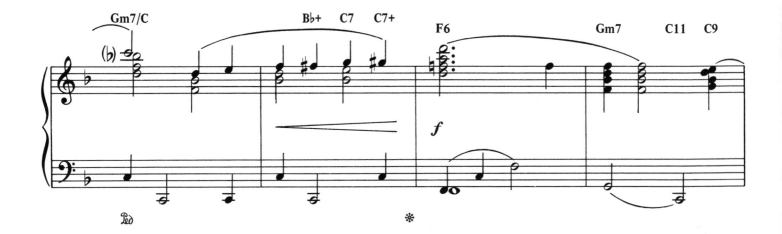

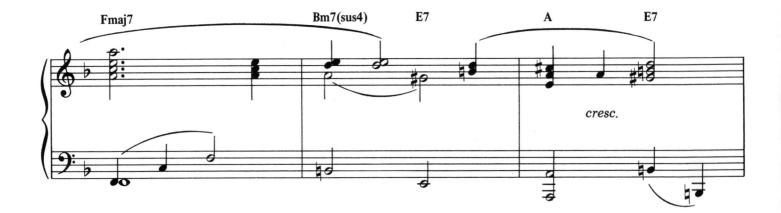

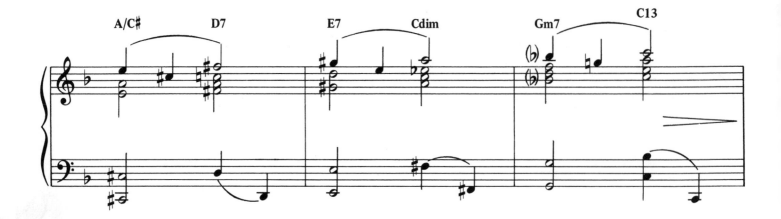

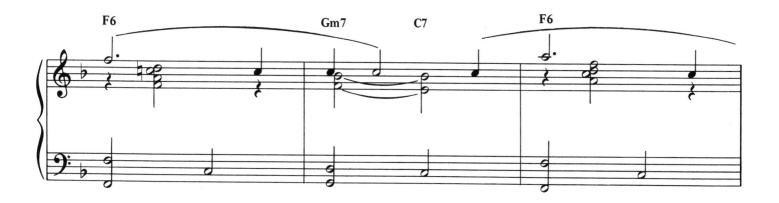

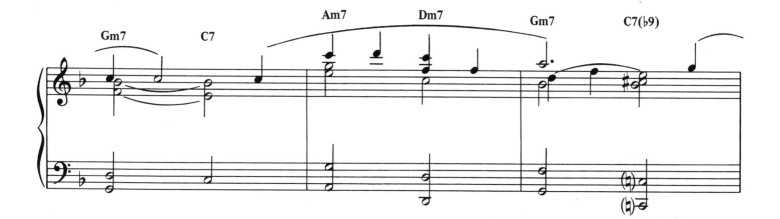

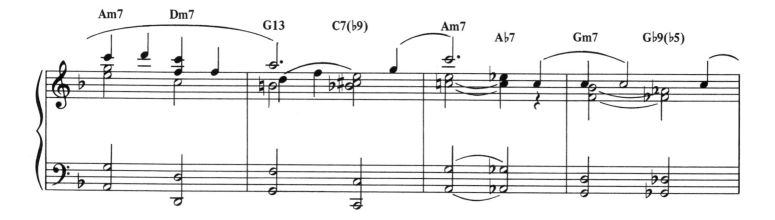

PICK YOURSELF UP

MUSIC BY JEROME KERN
WORDS BY DOROTHY FIELDS

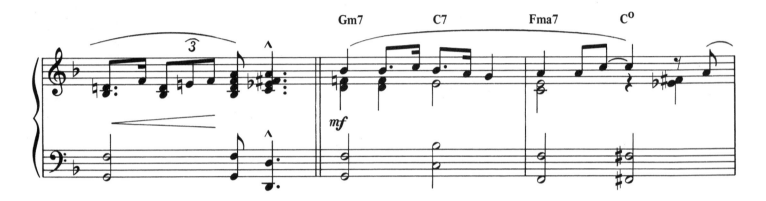

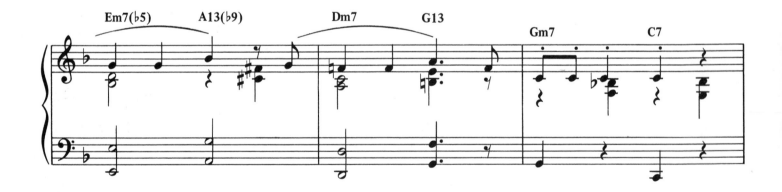

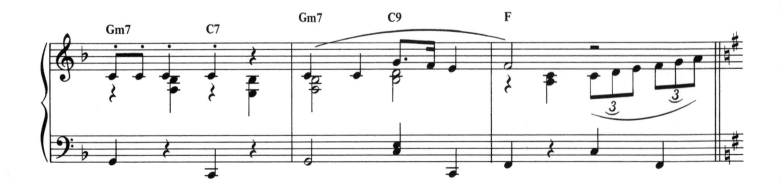

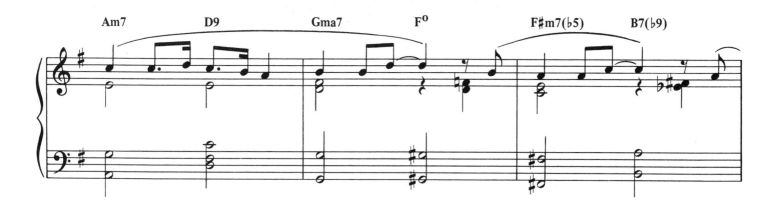

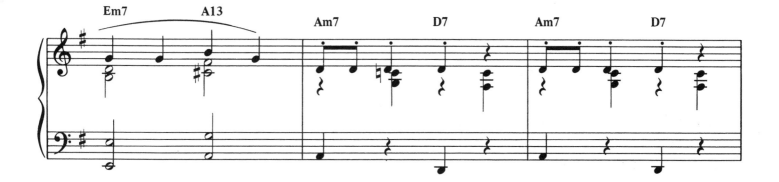

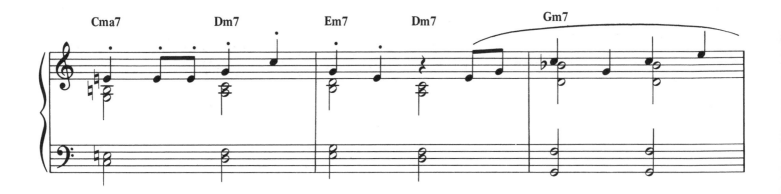

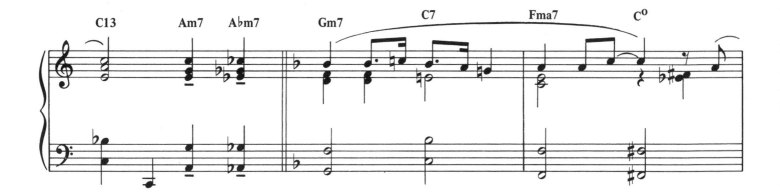

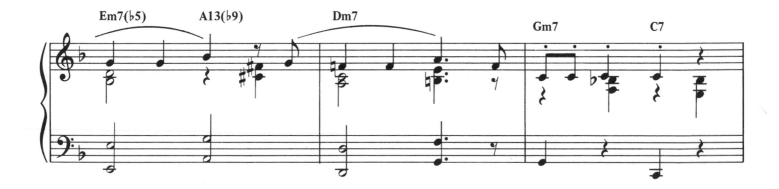

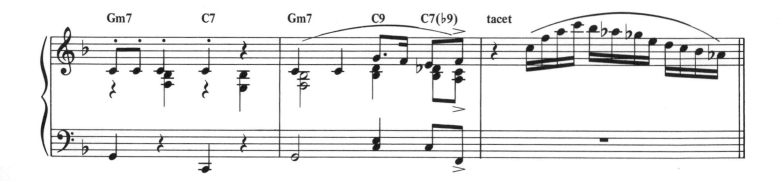

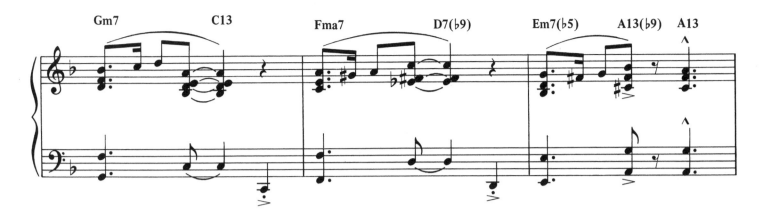

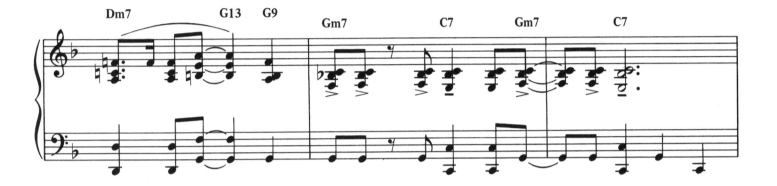

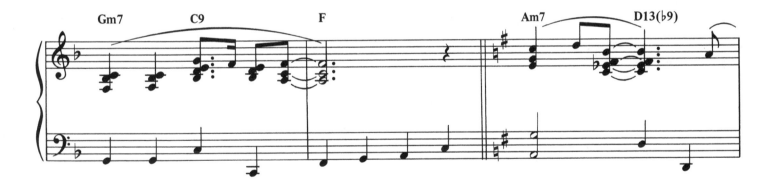

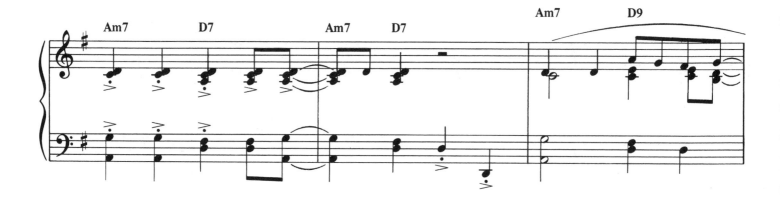

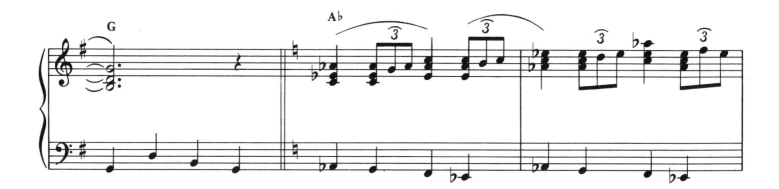

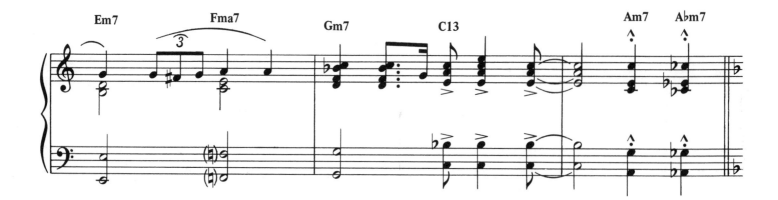

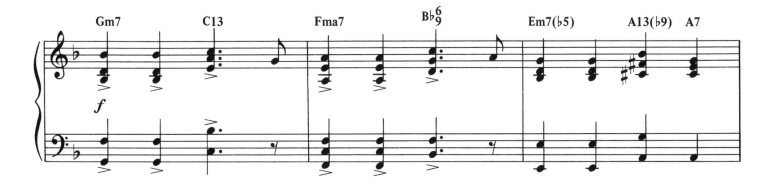

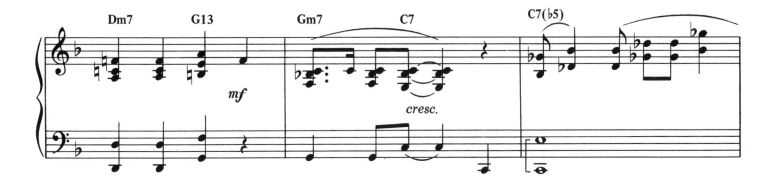

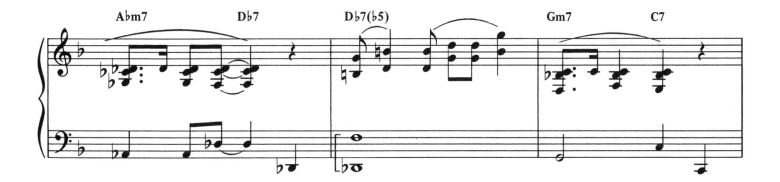

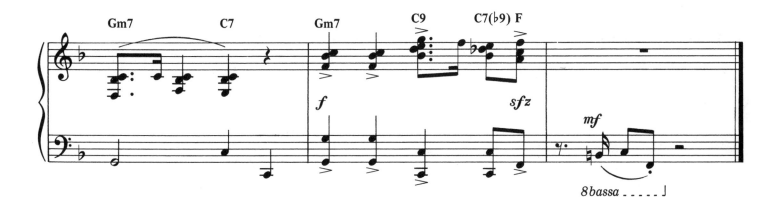

CAN'T HELP LOVIN' DAT MAN

MUSIC BY JEROME KERN
WORDS BY OSCAR HAMMERSTEIN II

Slowly, with expression

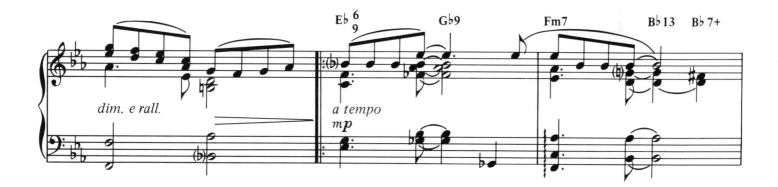

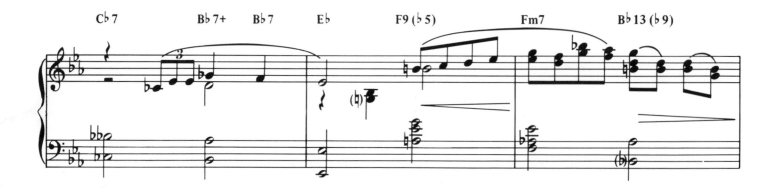

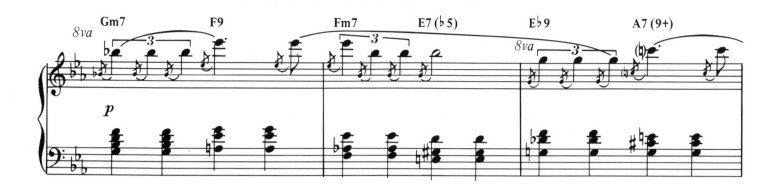

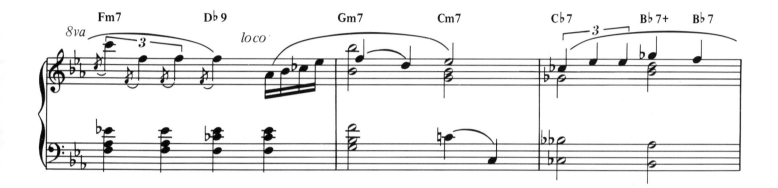

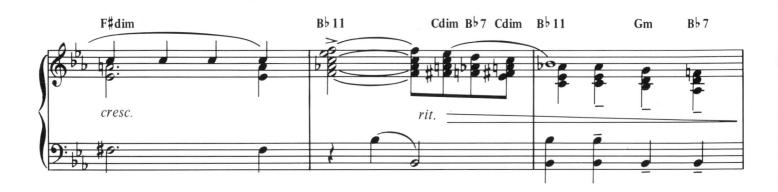

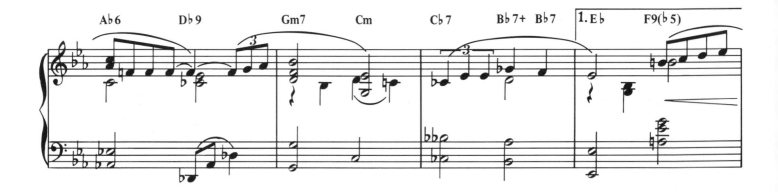

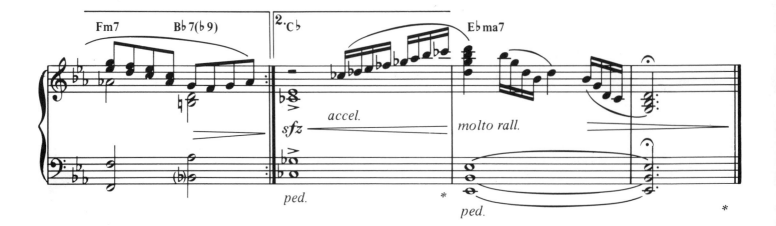

YOU COULDN'T BE CUTER

MUSIC BY JEROME KERN
WORDS BY DOROTHY FIELDS

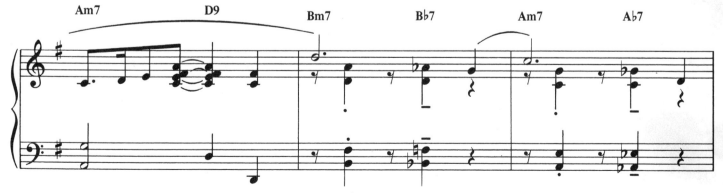

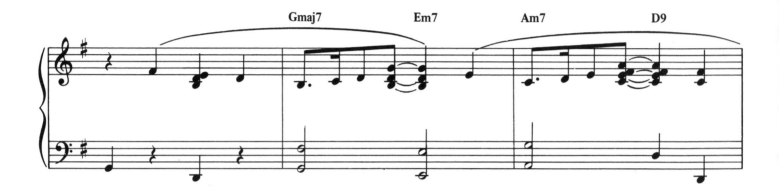

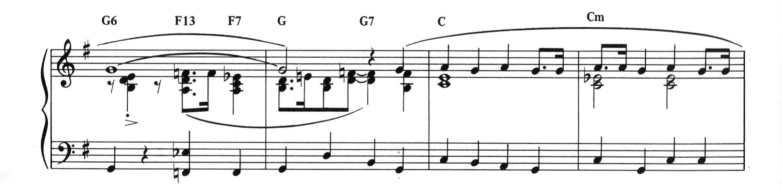

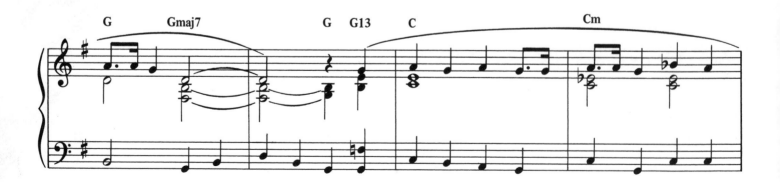

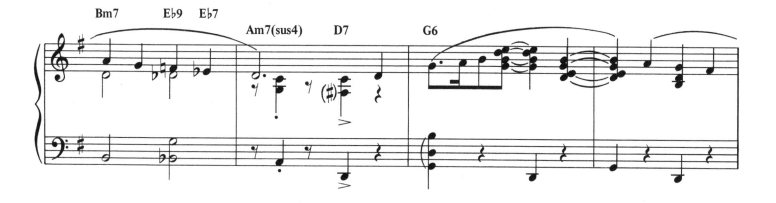

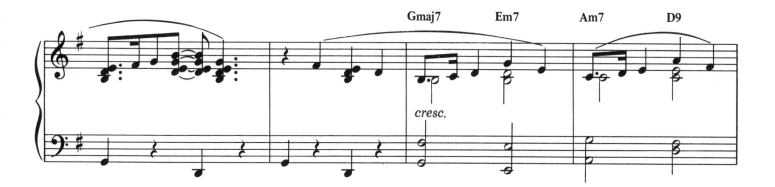

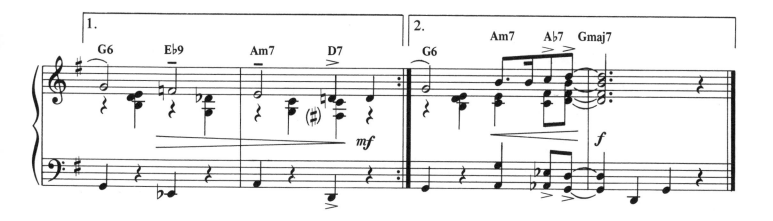

THE FOLKS WHO LIVE ON THE HILL

MUSIC BY JEROME KERN
WORDS BY OSCAR HAMMERSTEIN II

Moderately, with expression

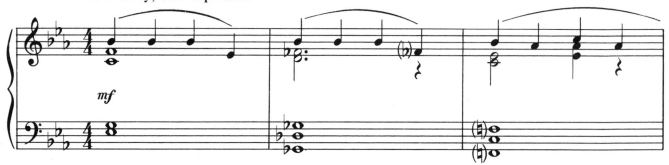

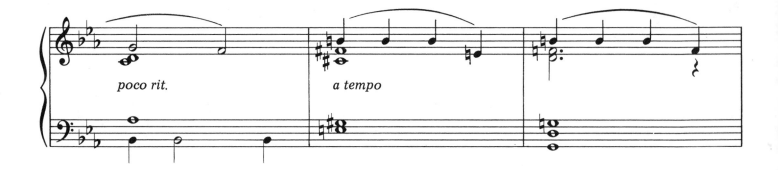

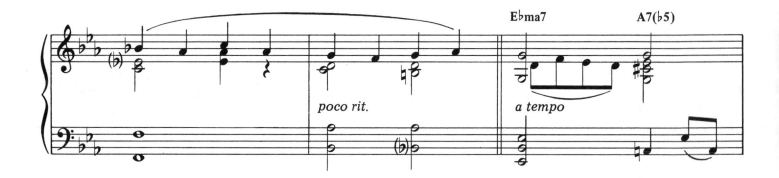

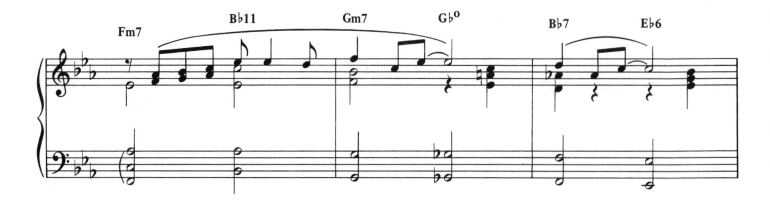

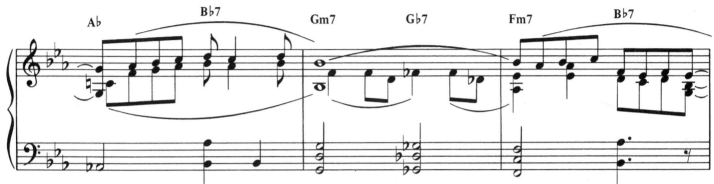

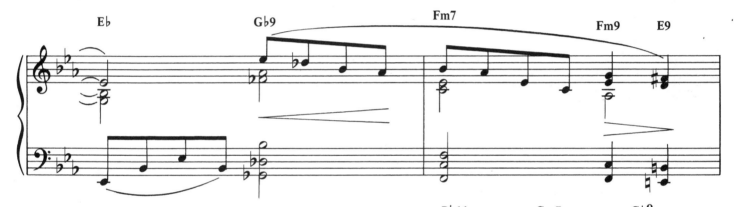

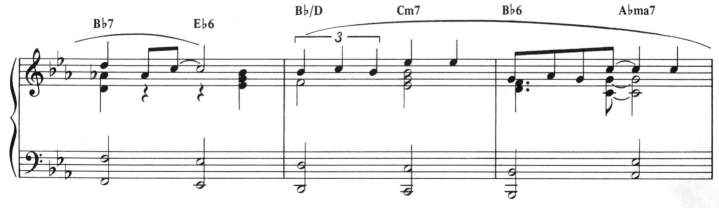

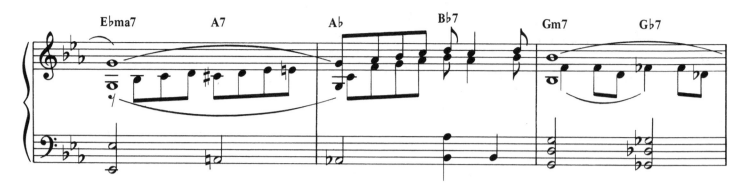

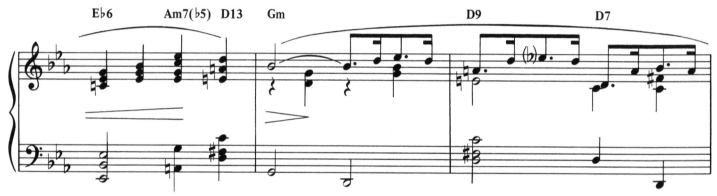

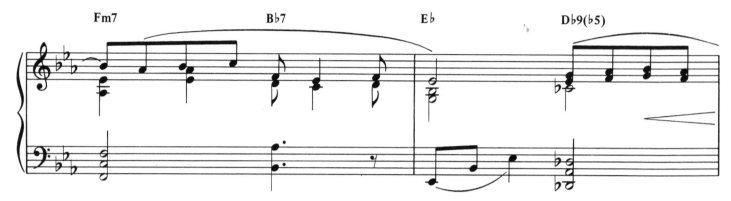

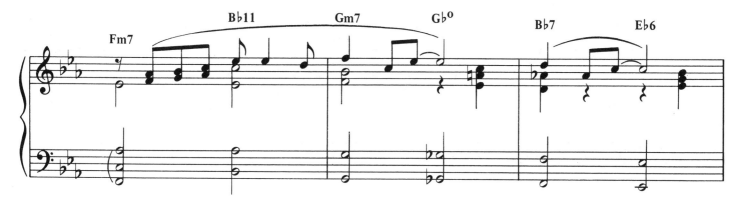

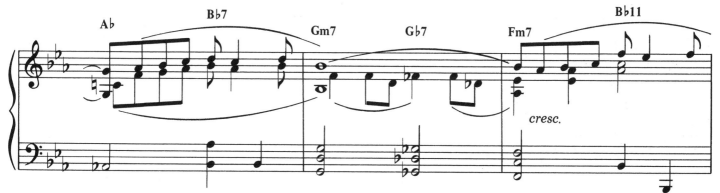

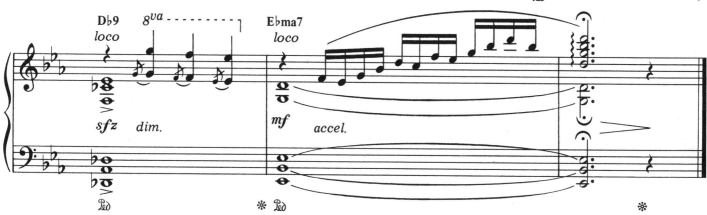

LONG AGO AND FAR AWAY

MUSIC BY JEROME KERN
WORDS BY IRA GERSHWIN

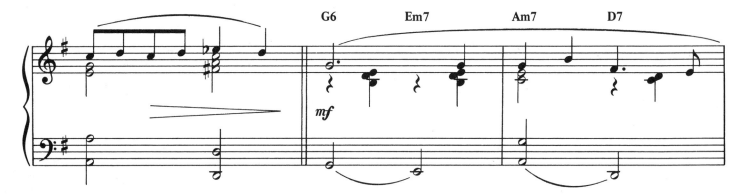

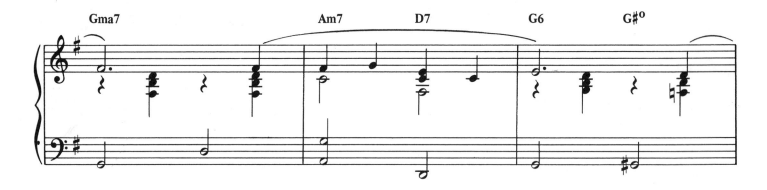

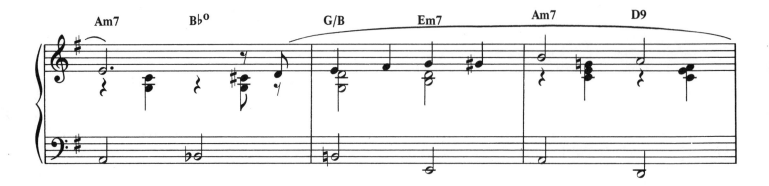

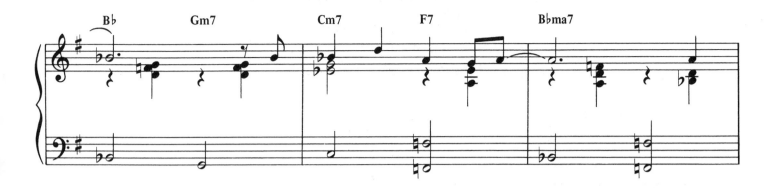

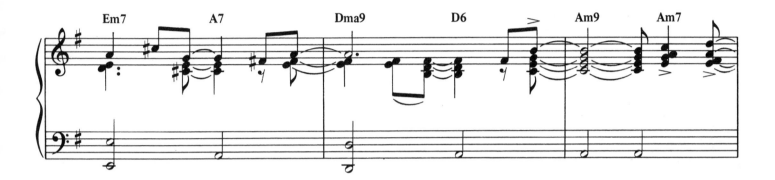

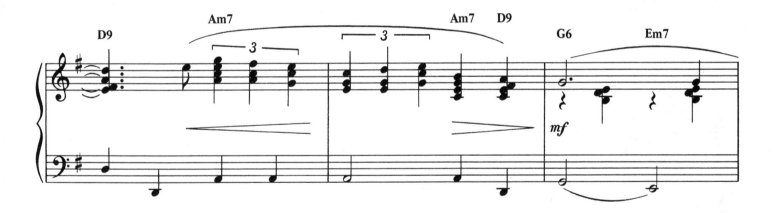

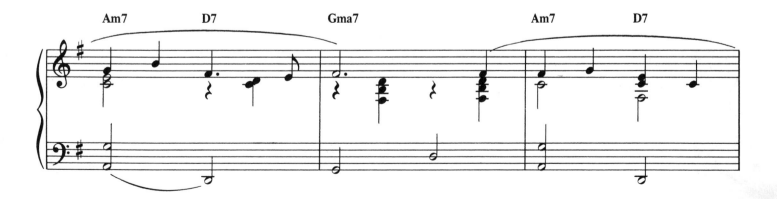

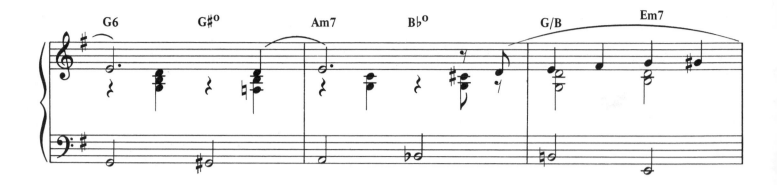

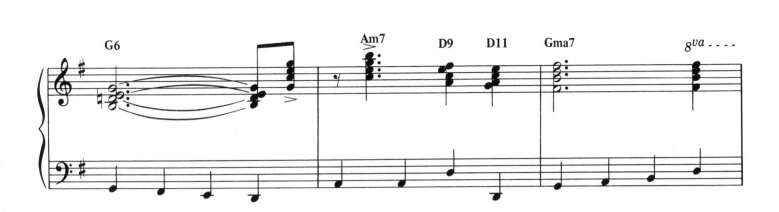

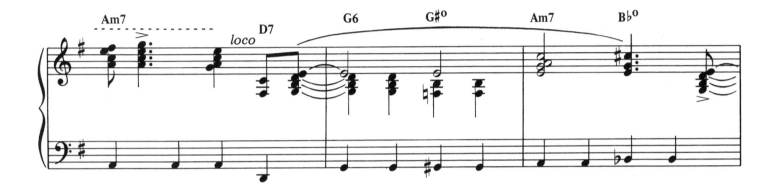

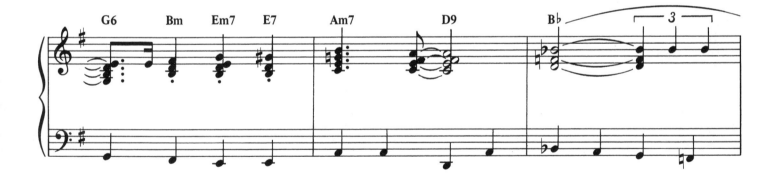

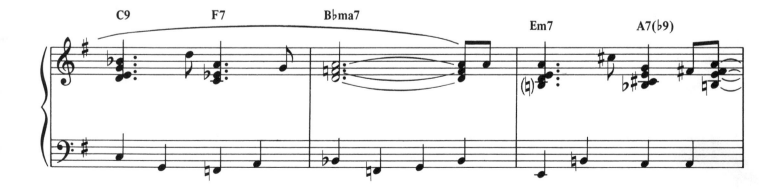

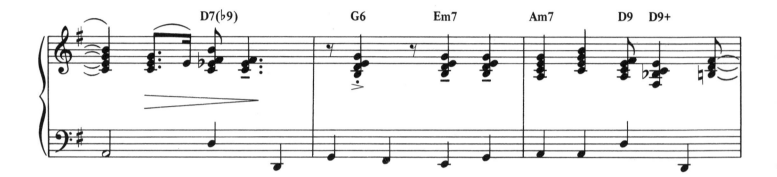

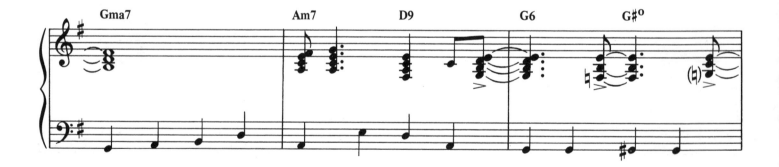

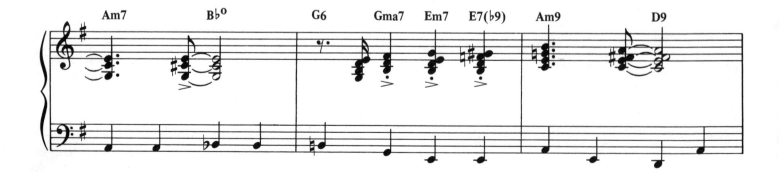

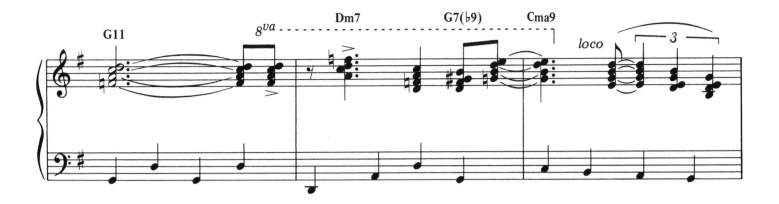

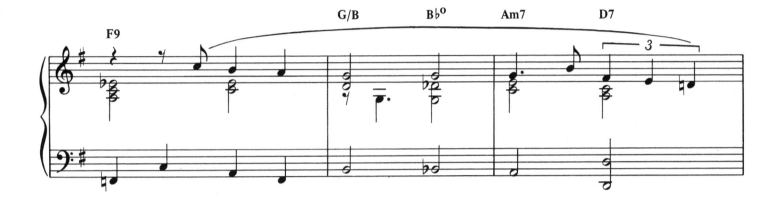

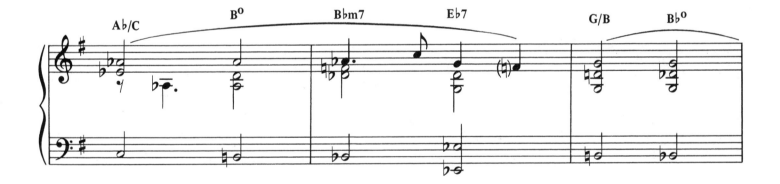

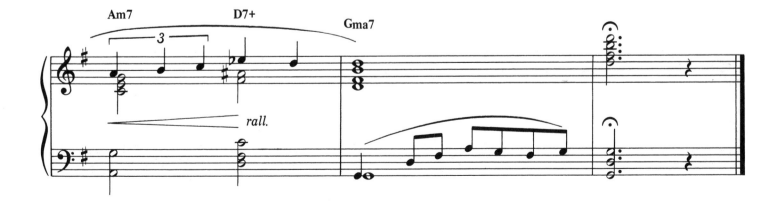

THE WAY YOU LOOK TONIGHT

MUSIC BY JEROME KERN
WORDS BY DOROTHY FIELDS

Moderately, with a jazz feel

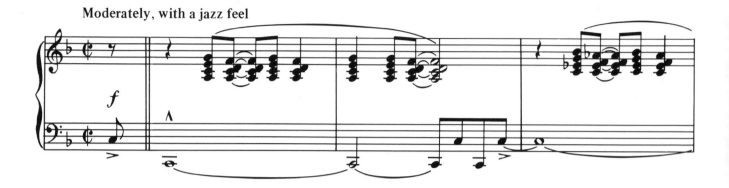

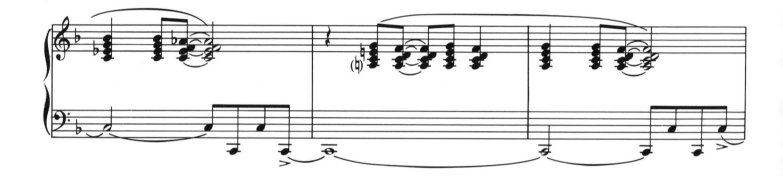

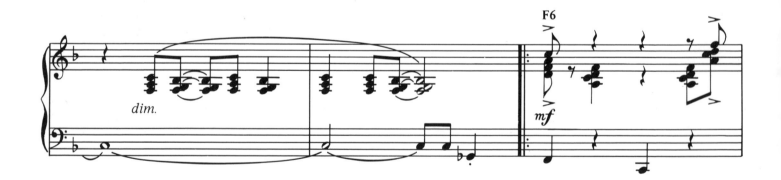

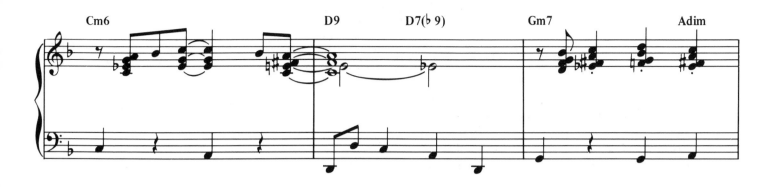

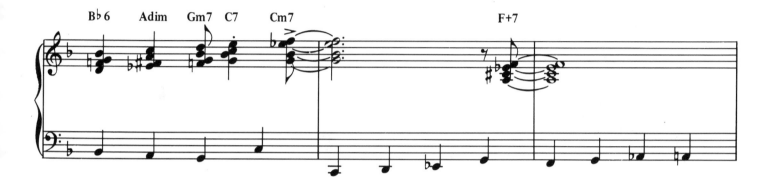

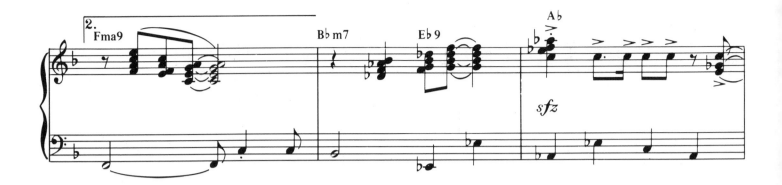

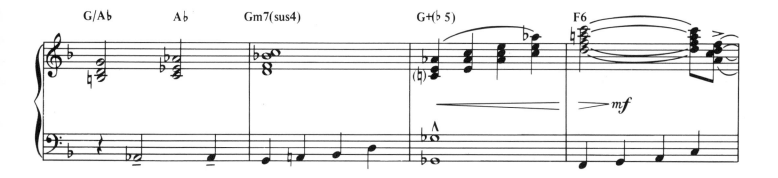

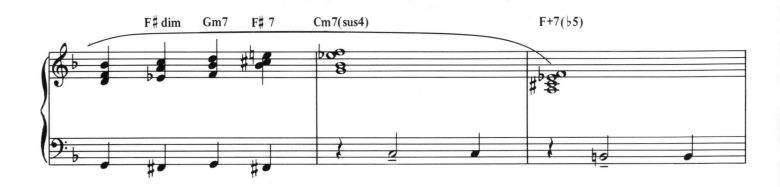

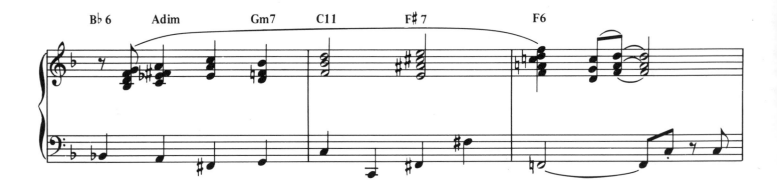

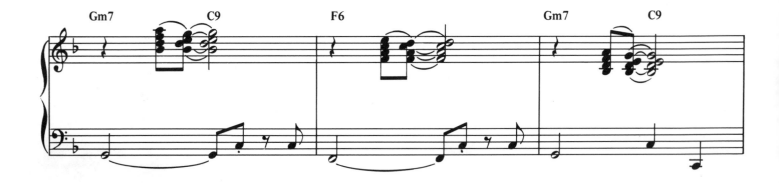

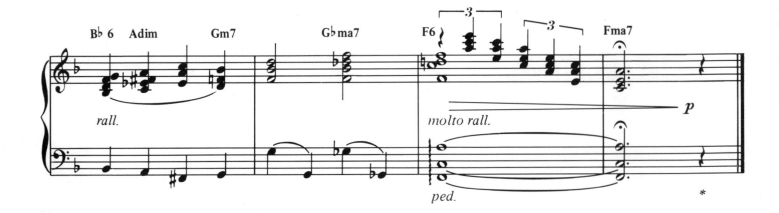

SMOKE GETS IN YOUR EYES

MUSIC BY JEROME KERN
WORDS BY OTTO HARBACH

Slowly (rubato)

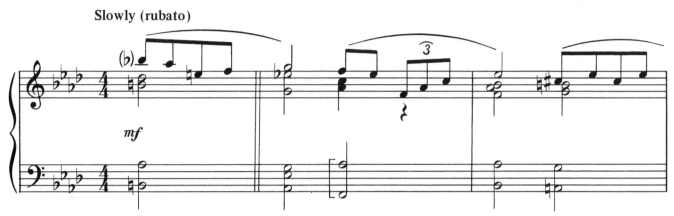

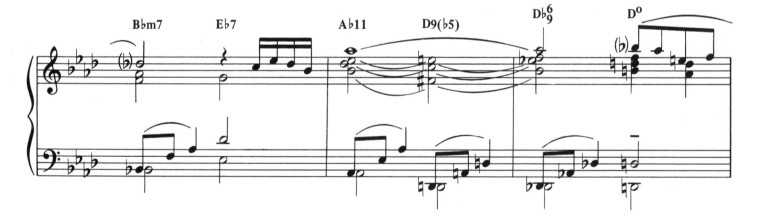

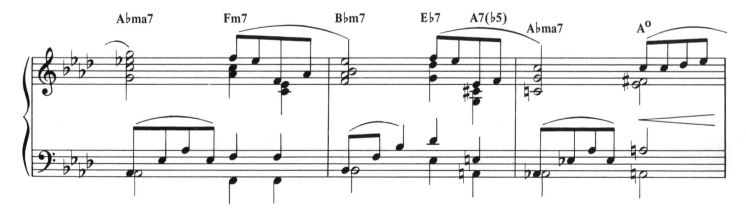

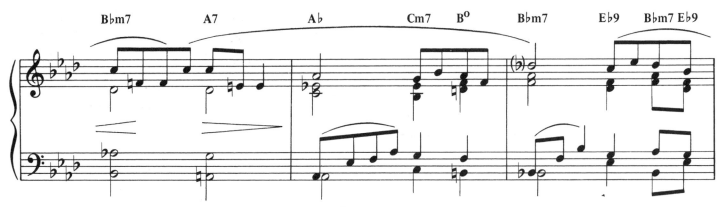

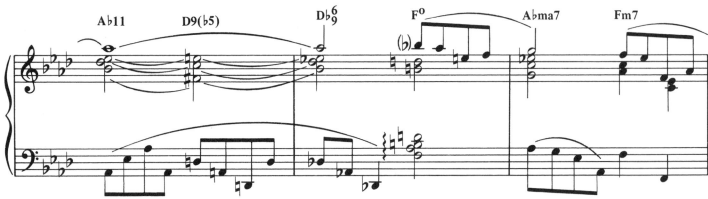

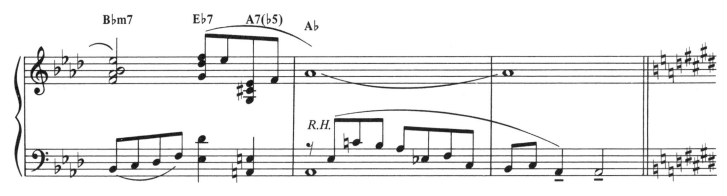

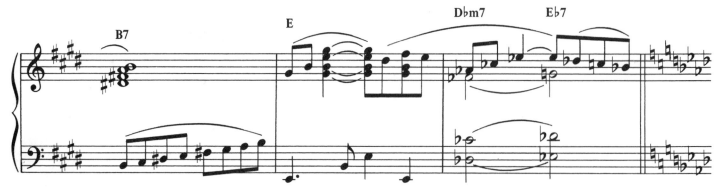

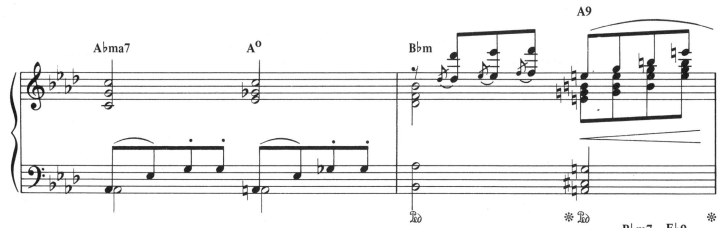
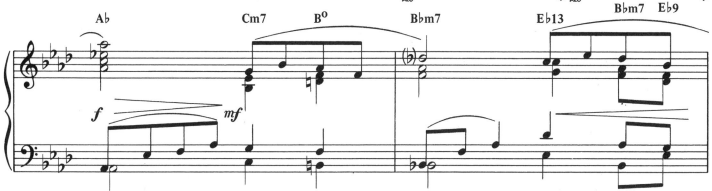

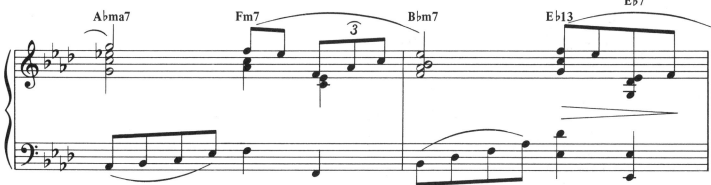
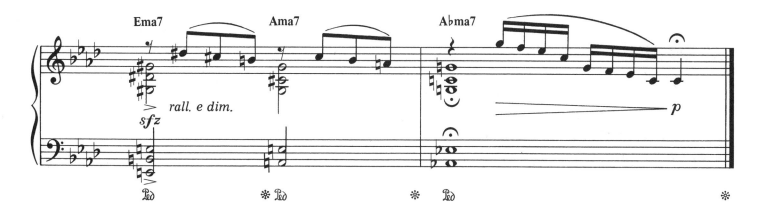

THE SONG IS YOU

MUSIC BY JEROME KERN
WORDS BY OSCAR HAMMERSTEIN II

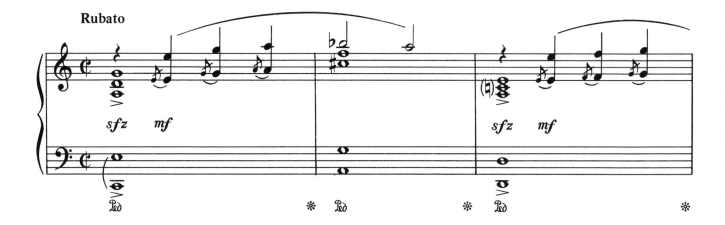

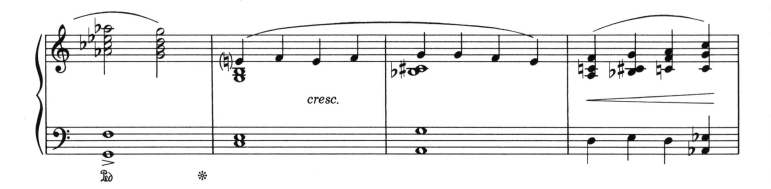

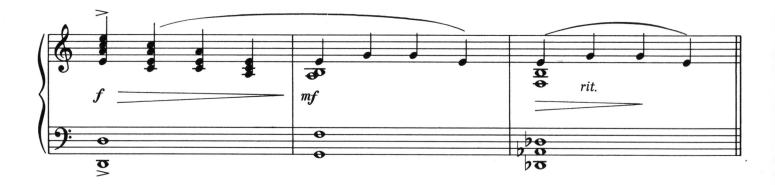

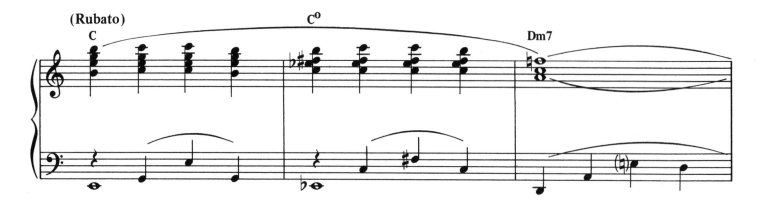

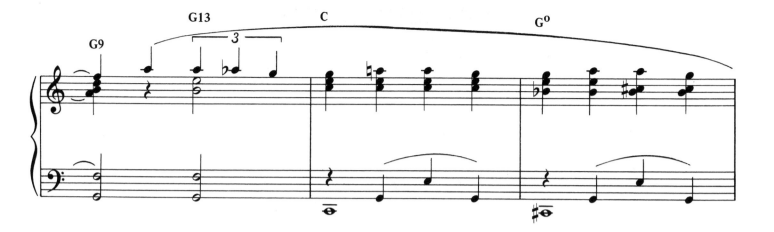

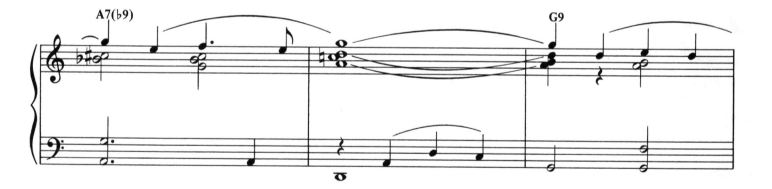

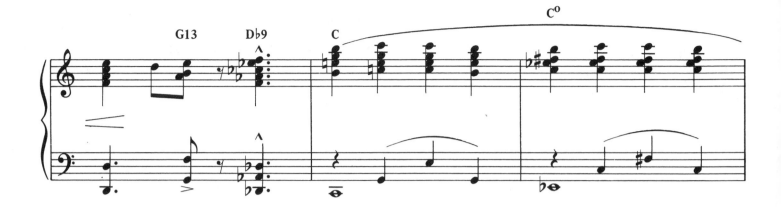

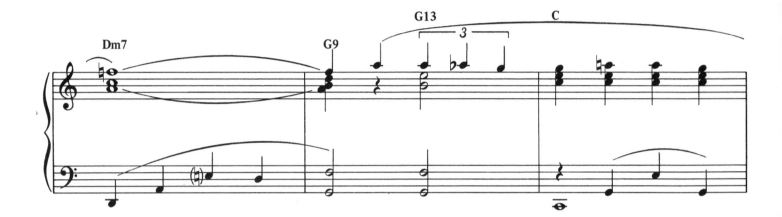

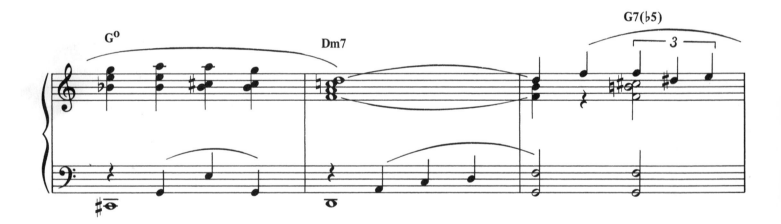

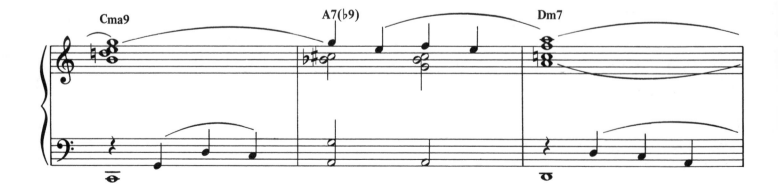

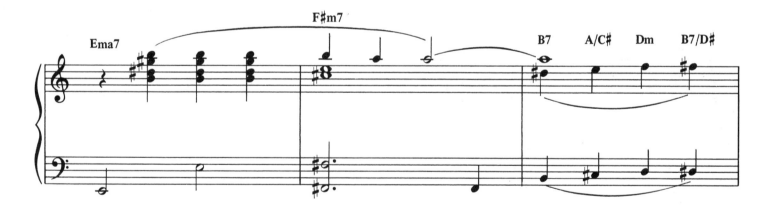

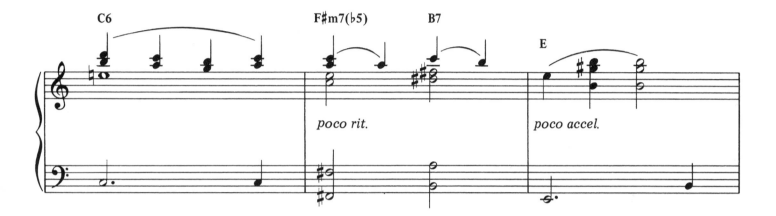

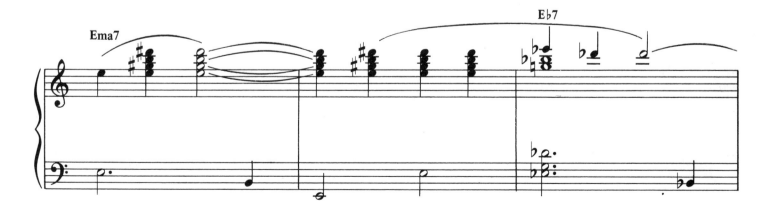

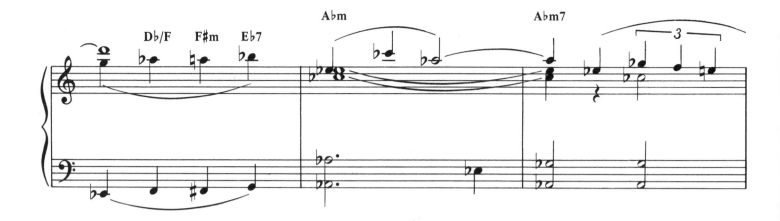

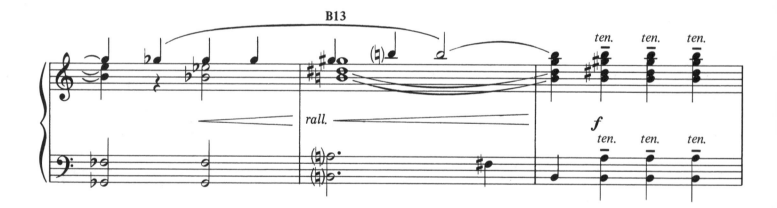

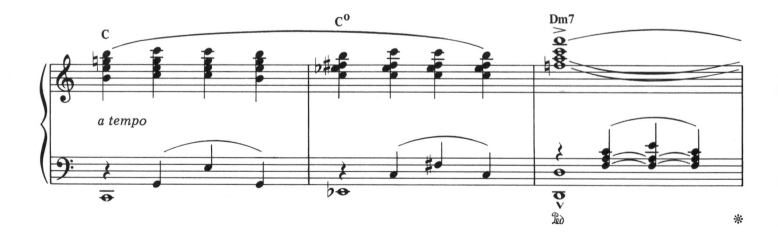

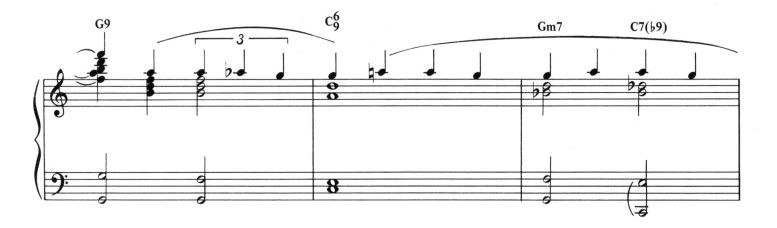

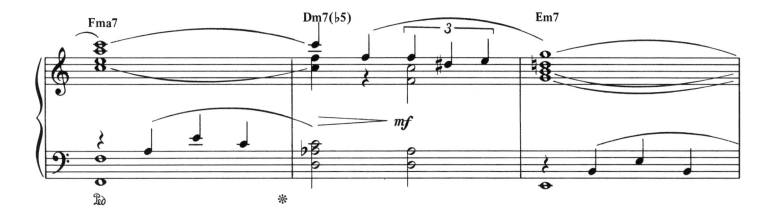

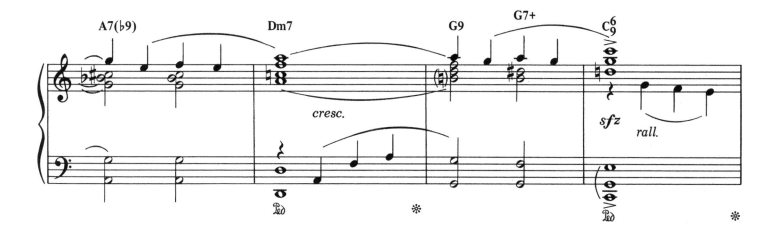

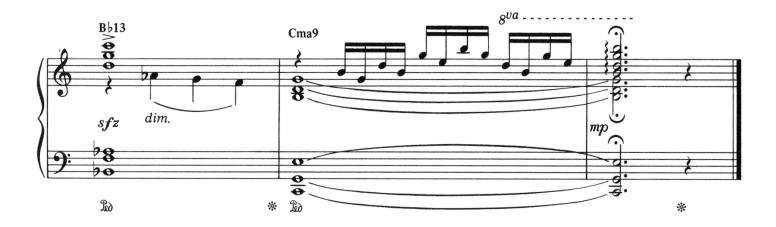

THEY DIDN'T BELIEVE ME

MUSIC BY JEROME KERN
WORDS BY HERBERT REYNOLDS

Moderately slow, with expression

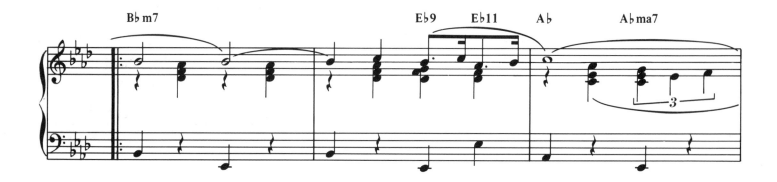

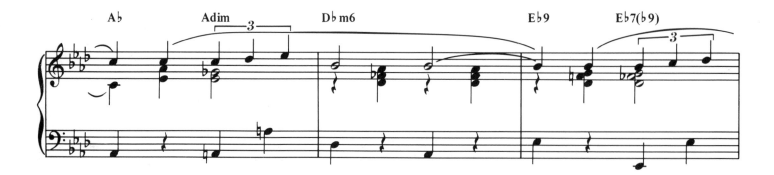

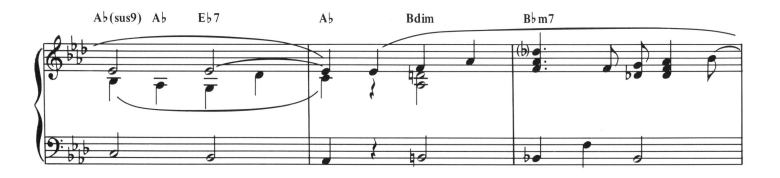

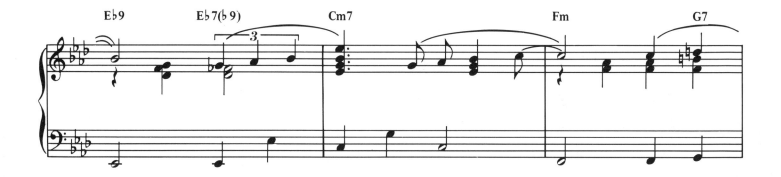

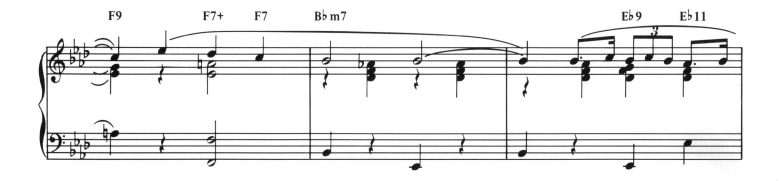

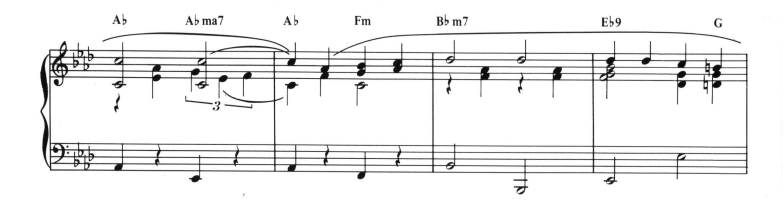

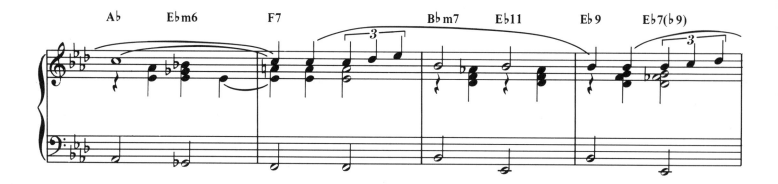

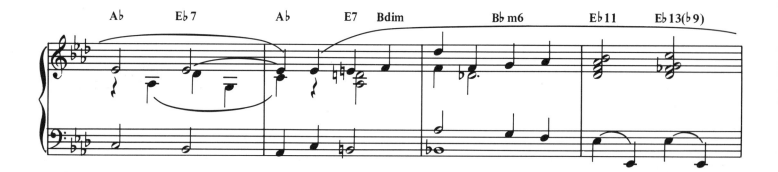

YESTERDAYS

MUSIC BY JEROME KERN
WORDS BY OTTO HARBACH

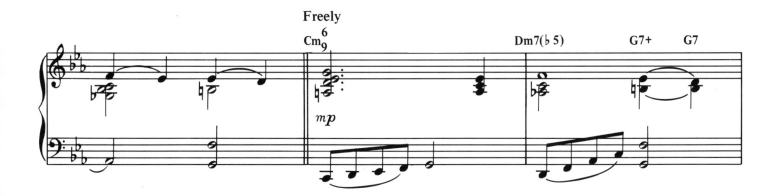

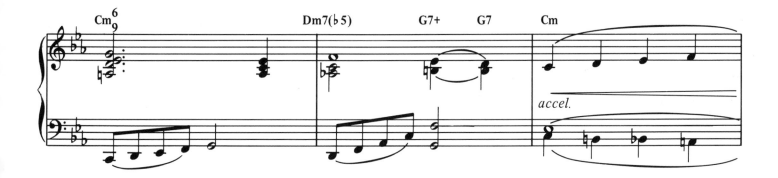

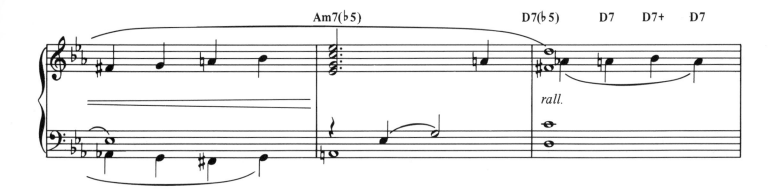

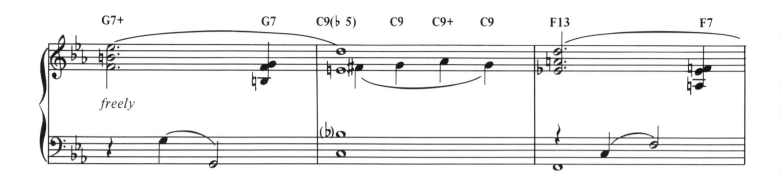

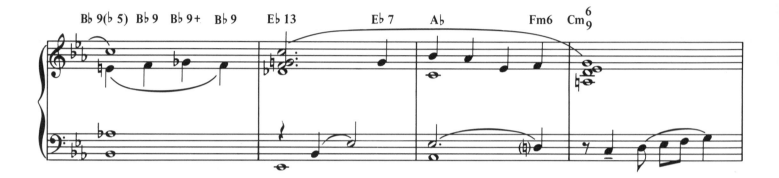

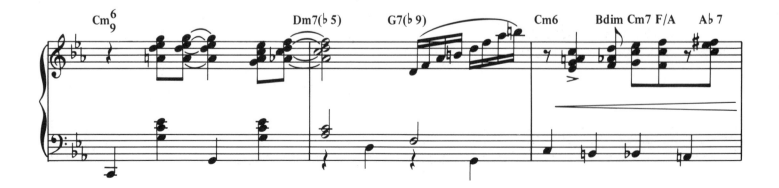

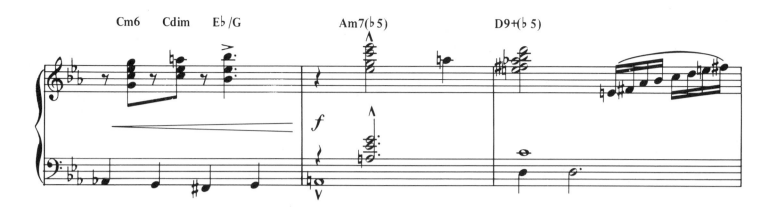

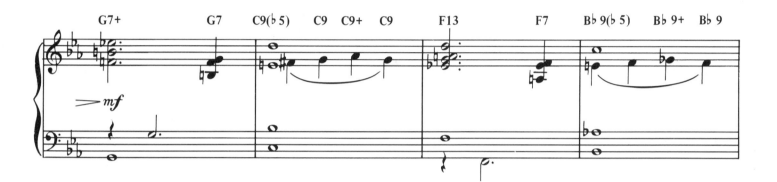

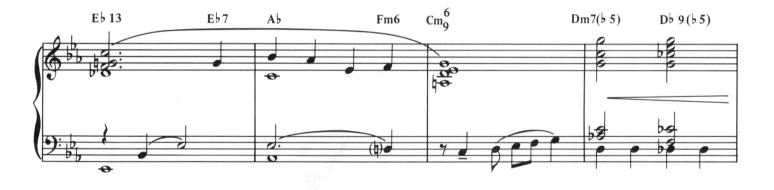